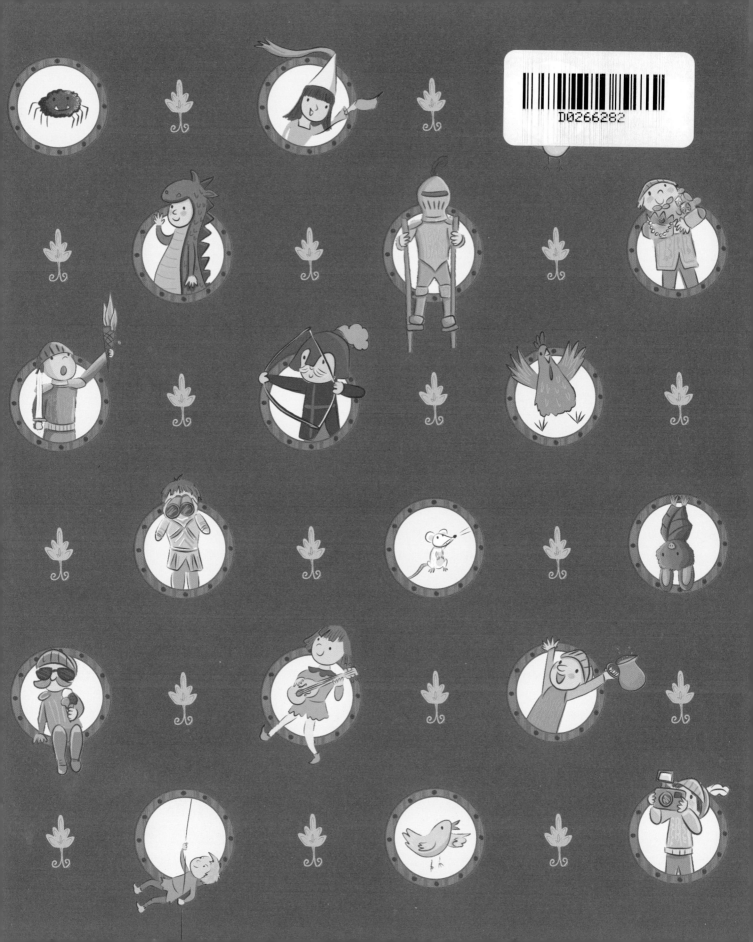

1001
Things to Find

1 towering castle

2 galloping horses

3 waving flags

4 shiny helmets

5 trusty shields

Knights

igloobooks

Can you find 1001 knight things?

Welcome, brave knights, to our noble medieval quest. The king and queen have offered a handsome prize for the retrieval of the golden dragon's egg. Are you brave enough to take on the challenge and journey to the dragon's lair?

In each scene you'll need to find Norman Knight, Belinda the Brave and a golden shield. There are over 1000 awesome things hiding among the pages for you to seek on your knight adventure.

Belinda the Brave

Norman Knight

The Golden Shield

Let's practise first. On the opposite page, see if you can spot Norman Knight, Belinda the Brave and the golden shield. Once you've found them, see if you can spot the items below, too.

7 fearless
archers

9 blue and
red flags

14 pairs of
binoculars

Round Table

The king has declared an emergency meeting! A ferocious dragon is guarding a precious egg and the king wants the knights to go and find it. Can you spot Norman Knight, Belinda the Brave and the golden shield?

3 stained-glass windows

4 twirly moustaches

5 pink tapestries

6 court jesters

7 creaky suits of armour

8 flaming torches

9 white mice

10 feather quills

13 wispy cobwebs

16 dripping candles

Jolly Jousting

Hear ye, hear ye! It's time for the Jolly Jousting Tournament and the king is on the search for new recruits to join the quest. Find Norman Knight, Belinda the Brave and the golden shield.

3 golden crowns

4 frilly handkerchiefs

5 grey horses

6 chain mail vests

7 pink helmet feathers

8 brown barrels

9 archery targets

10 red apples

13 blue arrows

16 muddy horse shoes

Farewell Fanfare

The town has thrown a parade to say farewell, as the brave knights begin the dangerous journey to the dragon's castle. Spot Norman Knight, Belinda the Brave and the golden shield.

4 potion bottles

6 clucking chickens

7 stinky fish bones

10 money pouches

14 pretty flowers

River Run

The knights' first obstacle is crossing a raging river. They must find a safe way across, or be swept away over the Wicked Waterfall! Find where Norman Knight, Belinda the Brave and the golden shield are hiding.

4 red canoes

6 stripy fish

7 paddling turtles

10 messages in a bottle

14 rubber rings

Muddled Maze

Uh, oh! It looks like the knights have taken a wrong turn and got lost in a forest maze. Let's hope they can find their way out. Can you find Norman Knight, Belinda the Brave and the golden shield?

3 digging shovels

4 floating kites

5 noisy megaphones

6 peeping periscopes

7 spinning compasses

8 big maps

9 hungry vultures

10 dirty footprints

13 brown ladders

16 floating balloons

Fantastic Funfair

Roll up, roll up, the Fantastic Funfair is in town. Luckily, our knights found their way out of the maze, so now they can have some fun! Find Norman Knight, Belinda the Brave and the golden shield.

3 food carts

4 knights on stilts

5 toy dragons

6 hairy coconuts

7 roller-coaster carrriages

8 yellow balloons

9 bumper cars

10 fluffy candyfloss

13 ticket stubs

16 boxes of popcorn

Cavernous Cave

Who turned out the lights? This creepy cave is full of things that go bump in the night. The knights need to find the way out, fast! Spot Norman Knight, Belinda the Brave and the golden shield.

4 poisonous mushrooms

6 yellow crystals

7 spooky pairs of eyes

10 friendly spiders

14 snoozing bats

Princess Tower

A fair maiden locked in a tower distracts our merry band of knights. Who locked her in, and what could be hiding in all that hair? Can you see Norman Knight, Belinda the Brave and the golden shield?

4 birds' nests

6 squeaky squirrels

7 tower windows

10 crash helmets

14 tall sunflowers

Bizarre Battle

Enemy knights are in sight! The knights must battle their way to the castle to get to the golden egg first. Water balloons at the ready! Find Norman Knight, Belinda the Brave and the golden shield.

3 long lances

4 lightning bolts

5 rotten tomatoes

6 wooden catapults

7 patterned umbrellas

8 purple feathers

9 archer's bows

10 white mice

13 water balloons

16 shiny swords

Castle Capture

Victory! The knights have finally reached the dragon's castle and must climb the walls any way they can to get inside to the egg. Where are Norman Knight, Belinda the Brave and the golden shield?

4 golden arrows

6 heavy cannons

7 green hooks

10 long ropes

14 spindly ladders

Treasure Trove

It turns out the dragon is actually very friendly. In exchange for an invite to a party at the castle, he will swap the precious golden egg. Spot Norman Knight, Belinda the Brave and the golden shield.

4 silver coins

6 pearl necklaces

7 green emeralds

10 red rubies

14 dazzling diamonds

Flying Fun

The dragon is giving the knights a ride back to the castle in style. Hang on as tight as you can and don't look down! Find Norman Knight, Belinda the Brave and the golden shield.

3 sparkling rainbows

4 pairs of sunglasses

5 beach balls

6 peanut butter sandwiches

7 treasure chests

8 playing cards

9 ice creams

10 yellow birds

13 dragon spines

16 fluffy clouds

Fabulous Feast

Hooray! The king is delighted with the egg and has thrown a party for their new dragon friend. Three cheers for the friendly dragon! Can you see Norman Knight, Belinda the Brave and the golden shield?

3 loud guitars

4 spiky pineapples

5 wrapped gifts

6 drinking goblets

7 jam tarts

8 jugs of juice

9 slices of cake

10 party hats

13 party poppers

16 special invitations

Hurrah! You've reached the end of the knights' quest and made a dragon friend along the way. Now, journey back through each page and see if you can find the special items below hidden in every scene.

A shiny
dragon scale

Headless Henry's
ghost

A secret
scroll

A shiny
coin

A jewel-encrusted
chest

The castle
cat

A golden
helmet

A flying
flag

How closely were you looking at each scene? Go back and see if you can spot where each of these items is still hiding.

Fairground
assistant

A set of
handprints

A worried
horse

A diving
knight

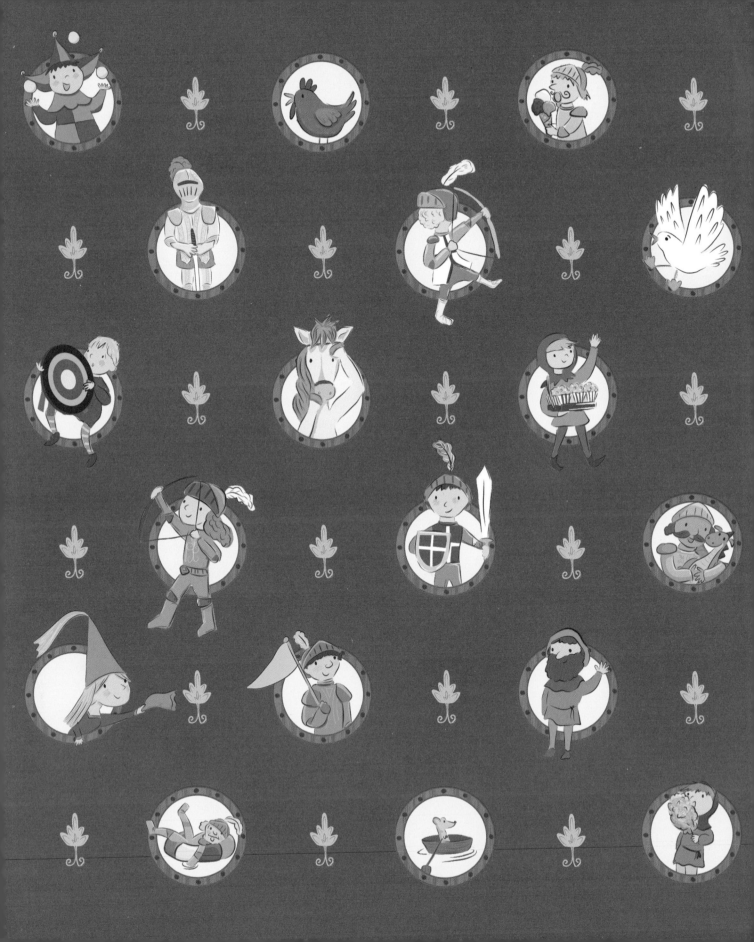